of it

part of

may be moving on, but I can honestly say that my heart and soul went into this place - and part of them remain. Please make sure that mission stays center to everything this place is about!

Mark A.

SIREN PRESS

Siren Interactive

1100 Lake St.

Oak Park, IL 60301

Foreword

Rare diseases are not really rare. Although each disease affects relatively few individuals, there are nearly 7,000 different types of rare diseases[1], so the number of individuals affected in the United States alone is close to 30 million. That's 1 in 10 of us! And many of those diagnosed are children who will have to cope with the disease throughout their lives.

No one understands the challenges of living with rare diseases better than caregivers. They face the daily challenges of nurturing these children, getting a correct diagnosis, accessing treatment, and managing finances and insurance. Many of these caregivers also work to raise funds for research and advocate for legislation that will support their children's needs.

In this book, you will meet some of these inspiring parents and get a glimpse of their lives.

---

1. National Institutes of Health Office of Rare Diseases Research. "Rare Diseases Frequently Asked Questions." http://raredisorders.info.nih.gov/file/Rare_Disease_FAQs.pdf

And you will see that, despite all the obstacles they must confront, these parents are paving the way to a brighter future for their children and for all rare disease caregivers and patients.

On behalf of the National Organization for Rare Disorders (NORD), we applaud this effort to bring hope, light, and awareness to the contribution these amazing caregivers make.

Peter L. Saltonstall,
President and CEO at National Organization for Rare Disorders

Introduction

Living with a rare disorder – or caring for someone with a rare disorder – can be lonely, frustrating, and frightening. It can also be an uplifting and affirming experience.

In this collection of inspiring stories, you'll meet some of the courageous parents who are traveling this road with their children.

These parents have dealt with passive doctors and nurses, more hospital visits than they can count, and a lack of knowledge, research, treatment, and financial support.

Yet, despite the many obstacles, all of these parents have found hope, empowerment, and purpose.

They have become parent detectives. They've created foundations when there were none. They've leveraged the power of the internet to connect with other families and doctors all over the world. They've held symposiums and have brought researchers together to collaborate and work towards a treatment or cure. They've supported others in similar situations through Facebook, Skype, Twitter, and their blogs. They've advocated in Washington D.C., and have worked tirelessly to raise awareness and funds – all while caring for their children.

Every day, these empowered parents are making a difference in their children's lives. Every day, they are also shaping the lives of future rare disease patients and the future of health care itself.

Share their joys, read about their hopes, be inspired by their dreams and their struggles, and celebrate with us the gift of these precious children.

To learn more, visit:

press.sireninteractive.com

Detective Moms

Finding the Answer When It's Never Been More Important

by Wendy White

"I realized that I, as her mother, am the one most responsible for making sure my daughter gets the best possible shot in life."

Many of the patients with rare disorders are not diagnosed by doctors, nurses, or researchers, but by a fierce and driven group of extraordinary detectives known as MOTHERS.

I should know. I'm one of them.

When my third child, Casey, was born, there was trouble right from the start.

I didn't get to hold her right away, as I had held my two sons. I remember looking over at the warming table and hearing the doctors and nurses talking to each other. I heard them say something about a club foot. I heard them talking about her low blood count. I remember them taking her to the nursery for more tests, and I remember them telling me that they were taking her across town to a teaching hospital for even more tests. I felt numb and out of control.

Ten hours later I checked out of the hospital where she was born to be with her at the teaching hospital, where they thought they'd be able to help her. But there weren't any solid answers.

Eight days later they let me take her home. She had a club foot, which they had casted, and they gave her a transfusion, but her blood count issue was inconclusive. I wasn't sure what to think, but I felt relieved. I trusted that the doctors were doing everything they could.

Every two weeks I took her back to the hospital to get her foot casted.

After four months, I was meeting with the resident instead of the surgeon when I went in for her recasting. I made an off-hand comment about her knees. I told him how interesting I thought it was that my daughter had dimpled knees when neither of my sons had had them. This obviously struck a bell with him and he left the room to consult with more doctors. Apparently, dimpled knees are not normal for any baby. This sent us down the rabbit hole again as she was given more tests. She had an x-ray, ultrasound, and finally an MRI.

The night after Casey had her MRI, I got a phone call from her surgeon. He told me they were sure that she didn't have kneecaps. He had never seen a patient like this, but he could tell me how the knee was supposed to work. He speculated that she would PROBABLY walk eventually, but climbing stairs might be a problem. This was a painful moment.

That weekend I went to my church, which was not handicapped-accessible. I stood in the entry way, looking up at all those stairs.

I think it was right after this that I realized that I, as her mother, am the one most responsible for making sure she gets the best possible shot in life. I was done with guessing.

I became a mom detective.

I must have visited 10 hospitals, and I read everything I could get my hands on about knees and blood and club feet. I spent a huge amount of time following promising threads on the internet. In my search, I found a paper by a researcher who had identified the genetic marker for a disorder called nail-patella syndrome. I tracked him down at Johns Hopkins and talked to him about Casey. He didn't know any doctors in Chicago who had experience with this disorder, but he did tell me there was a conference every two years that I could take her to.

At my next visit with Casey's doctor, I laid out all the information I had found on the internet and told her about my conversation with the researcher at Johns Hopkins. She took my papers and went into the back of her office. She came back out five minutes later and told me, "I think you are right; I think she has nail-patella syndrome." I felt relieved, but I wasn't sure where we were going from there.

I couldn't wait two years for that conference, so I went back to Dr. Google.

There are nearly 7,000 rare disorders. Even though each one is different, by some estimates rare disorders affect one in ten people, and 80 percent of them are children. There are potentially 30,000,000 people – just in the United States! – with rare disorders. And I guarantee you, there are hundreds of thousands of mothers, fathers, and grandparents out there looking for answers, searching for any information they can find so that they aren't blindsided and can make sure that they are doing the best they can for their children, whatever the outcome.

At that point, I would have taken good information from anyone who could give me something that I believed would help my child. If there had been a therapy that would have helped her, I would have been all over that, too. I changed my surgeon on the advice of my physical therapist because I trusted her medical opinion and knowledge of the system.

During the time that I was looking for help for Casey, I was also involved with technology and running a web design firm. I knew technology was changing how we live, form relationships, and solve problems. I actually already had clients dealing with rare diseases. But this experience showed me how much more I could do in my professional life to support people like me.

So my personal journey with my daughter led me to refocus my company completely, helping grow the relationships among all of those who are working to support people with rare disorders.

As a web person, I knew we needed to find an easier way to get these folks together. We needed a database of symptoms or a Facebook for caregivers, not just for diagnosis, but for treatment, for compassion, and for emotional support.

Two years ago I started volunteering with the National Organization for Rare Disorders (NORD), and I helped them launch Rare Disease Day in the U.S. on the last day of February each year. In 2009 we launched a campaign called Alone We Are Rare, Together We Are Strong. I know that all of us working together can make a difference.

Casey's condition is called nail-patella syndrome. I have so much hard-won information for parents of anyone with this disorder, including the following tips:

- **Pay attention to how your child moves, not just if she or he complains.**

- **Find a great physical therapist and get started right away.**

- **Go out of your way to find other people who have the same condition.**

We haven't met anyone with her condition yet,

but through my contacts I've learned that a three-year-old girl with nail-patella syndrome is moving into our area. Casey can't wait to meet her, and I think it'll be very good for that little girl to meet Casey.

Casey walks and can handle stairs, although she wears leg braces at night. She plays violin and she sings. Casey also plays soccer. It's hard for her to run, so she isn't out on the field, but she is the toughest goalie you'll ever meet.

It isn't only people who have rare disorders and their families who should care about these issues. Rare diseases affect us all because innovation happens at the margins. As I heard Dr. Tim Cote, the head of the orphan and neglected disease department of the FDA say, "Everything we know about the human condition, we've learned from people with rare disorders. Someone is born missing an enzyme or factor or some other problem and we figure out how to solve it. We learn from this and move on."

Casey also likes to read. A few months ago she

got a book from the library on famous American women. After she read it she told me she had a new hero: Wilma Rudolph. Wilma Rudolph had polio and wore leg braces in the 1940s, but then grew up to win three Olympic Gold Medals.

About the Author

Wendy White, founder and president of Siren Interactive Corp., is an innovative leader who has been working for over a decade at the intersection of health care, patient empowerment, and online marketing to facilitate improved patient outcomes.

Siren Interactive, a relationship marketing agency focused exclusively on rare disorders, enables biopharmaceutical clients to use the power of the internet to establish credible, trusting relationships with patients, caregivers, and healthcare professionals through education, support, and service. Siren, which was just named to the Inc. 5000 list of fastest-growing, private companies in America, focuses exclusively on rare diseases. This bold marketing strategy illustrates Wendy's vision for how the internet can facilitate the type of interactions that can pull together previously isolated sufferers and their caregivers into productive communities that can work together to provide real, bottom line impact in quality of life.

To learn more about rare diseases or donate to the National Organization for Rare Disorders, visit:

www.RareDiseases.org

Feeling 'Not Alone'

Power of Community Brings Answers, Opportunities

by Catherine Calhoun

"Through the internet, I have the power to reach out to doctors, moms, and researchers all over the world… I've found that sharing our story helps me feel not so alone. It also helps other families when we share our stories. Sometimes the stories make you cry, sometimes they make you laugh, but they always make you feel not alone. I live in this little town and I can connect with people all over the world."

It was a Monday, and as I was dropping my two kids off at school I noticed my four-year-old son limping. Billy wasn't complaining about any pain but it worried me, so I decided to pick him up early from school and take him to the doctor's office.

Billy's doctor ordered an x-ray of his hip, so we drove over to the local hospital for the x-ray. Once the results came in, I knew something was wrong. The nurses avoided my eyes and wanted to discuss the results with the doctor alone. Eventually, I was informed that Billy had lesions all over his bones.

I had so many questions and very few answers. Were the lesions cancerous? Billy was referred to a children's hospital in New Orleans, two hours away (this appointment was set for the very next morning). As soon as I stepped out of the local hospital's x-ray area, I immediately called my friends and asked them to start Googling.

That Tuesday at the children's hospital in New Orleans, the bone doctors ordered more x-rays, this time on every bone in Billy's body. The doctors seemed baffled; they had never see anything like this before and whispered the names of possible diseases.

The next day, a Wednesday, Billy and I drove back to New Orleans to meet with another doctor for a second opinion. We met with this bone doctor and a team of four medical students. During the appointment, I wondered aloud if the birthmarks on Billy's back were related to the lesions on Billy's bones. Suddenly the doctor and students were buzzing and the atmosphere of the room immediately changed. Earlier that week, the doctor and medical students had completed a rare disease bone study and learned about a rare disorder called McCune-Albright syndrome. They were positive that Billy's symptoms matched those of McCune-Albright patients. In less than three days' time, Billy's diagnosis was confirmed.

McCune-Albright syndrome, described in 1937 by Donovan James McCune and Fuller Albright, is a genetic disorder of bones (fragile bones called fibrous dysplasis) and skin pigmentation, and causes hormonal problems. After Billy's diagnosis, I worked my hardest to pay attention to as much information as I could. After a few online searches, I discovered the Major Aspects of Growth In Children (MAGIC) Foundation and immediately became a member. As a member, I was able to access all of their old newsletters. In one article, a bone doctor in Florida expressed very different opinions than Billy's current doctor. My husband, Kevin, immediately faxed the article to our doctor, who was very grateful for the information we had found and showed interest in working with the bone doctor in Florida. We all wanted to learn as much as we could so we could sit down and make a plan for the future.

The reason for the limping? It was a tiny fracture in Billy's femur, at the top where the femur bone connects into his hip. The x-rays showed that in both of his femurs this spot where the bone connects into the hip was very weak (usually the femur is the strongest bone in the body). Billy couldn't even think of walking again until the doctors placed a metal rod in each femur for support (kind of like the metal bars or "rebar" placed in concrete for buildings). The rods are literally screwed into the small amount of "good" bone he has at the top of each femur.

In the meantime, Billy's doctor advised us to discourage Billy from walking even a step. If Billy fell, his bones could easily shatter beyond repair. To our surprise, Kevin and I didn't have any problem getting Billy to stop walking. While we prepared to take the next steps, Billy spent the next few months scooting himself around the house.

Four months and a lot of preparation later, Billy finally had his first surgery. We were really nervous and waited close to four hours (about two hours for each leg) in the waiting room area with friends trying to have normal conversations and do normal things like eat lunch and joke about the never-ending clicking and whirring of the huge ball machine sitting in the hospital lobby.

It was a relief to be called into the recovery area and see Billy's sweet face. After a while, he ate a popsicle and told his doctor that next time he would take an "orange one." It was downhill from there as we tried to manage his pain. Kevin and I both still get knots in our stomachs when we think about it. Within a few weeks Billy was going to physical therapy three times a week and counting each step he could take.

Billy is on his second set of metal rods right now. These will probably be replaced in the next year. Sometimes when you have a medically complex kid, you think you should be a "pro" at things like medical appointments and surgeries and not worrying so much. I found it really comforting, though, when another mom from the MAGIC Foundation told me that "surgery is scary every single time and it's okay to ask for support every single time."

The second bone surgery was better than the first because we knew what to expect and did better with pain management. It does, however, get harder physically for his caregivers because he gets bigger, and transferring someone who is fragile and in pain is nerve-racking.

After every one of these bone surgeries, Billy has had to relearn how to stand and walk. Although he is persistent and eventually gets it each time, he's never been able to walk as well as he could before the first surgery. This is very painful for us. The doctors made it sound like the problem could be fixed with the rods, and we assumed he would just recover and things would go back to the way they were. With each surgery, Billy loses his ability to walk far and fast and now uses either a wheelchair or a walker to get around. It took our family awhile to accept this outcome. And some family members sometimes still say things like, "I can't believe that he has never walked as well again – he doesn't even walk as well as his four-year-old self."

Billy's big hormone issue from the McCune-Albright was having a fast thyroid (called hyperthyroidism). It was hard for his doctors to make sure his thyroid levels were safe for his bone surgeries. To ensure Billy could safely cope with the many bone surgeries to come, we traveled to Connecticut to have his thyroid removed when he was six. After the surgery he had a long cut across his neck. I wasn't sure what kind of reaction to expect from Billy after the bandages were removed. I didn't know if he would care or be grossed out. When we were taking the bandages off together, I remember him looking at the long scar and saying:

"This is awesome! I look so tough!" I was amazed at how different and positive his perception could be from my own expectations.

Today our family has gotten over the initial shock, we have a doctor we trust, and we believe we have Billy in a good situation. But we do feel alone sometimes and that makes it hard. Luckily, we have the internet. I don't know what I would do without it. We have been able to ask parents questions as well as answer other parents' questions.

For example, Billy has lots of bone pain and it worries me. A researcher friend and a Google search helped me find the best bone pain researcher in the country. I contacted him with some questions. He responded honestly and told me he knew very little about Billy's disease. I asked him if he would be interested in doing some research if we could get enough funding together, and thankfully he said yes. I met another rare-disease mom online and I asked her how she set up her research fund. She told me how she did it and gave me some tips. Our family decided to set a goal to raise $5,000 for the research fund each year, and since August 2010, we have raised $4,000.

I feel good knowing I am doing something that will help people like Billy in his lifetime. Through the internet, I have the power to reach out to doctors, moms, and researchers all over the world. I also blog, and I've found that sharing our story helps me to feel not so alone. It also helps other families when we share our stories. Sometimes the stories make you cry, sometimes they make you laugh, but they always make you feel not alone. I live in this little town and I can connect with people all over the world.

I became an official volunteer for the MAGIC Foundation in 2008. Every week I talk to grown-up siblings and moms of kids who have been diagnosed from around the world. Sometimes it's just nice for them to talk to someone who understands what the medical terms mean. These talks have shown me how powerful a mother's love for her child really is – it's like nuclear energy. I don't think there's anything as powerful as when you get a bunch of these moms together. We're on a bittersweet journey, but maybe it takes something like this to make you a better person.

Today Billy is a sweet and funny eight-year-old. He faces challenges every day and yet he always has such a positive perspective. There's a sweet little magic about him and it spills onto me. Billy has a working dog named Picasso, and the two of them are so large in personality. I like taking Picasso out with us because people don't make sad faces when Picasso is around. They no longer see just a kid in a wheelchair.

Recently we enrolled Billy in wheelchair tennis. When Billy saw the other kids and young adults whizzing around the court, he was so excited. Even though he is only eight, I think he recognizes the power of community. There is a gift in the health challenges for Billy; he has more courage than most adults I know, and that's worth a lot. Sometimes you wish you could make things easy for your kids, but success is a lot about attitude and hard work. Billy is not bitter. This is the life he has, and we are doing our best to empower him along the way.

About the Author

Catherine Calhoun is a writer and mother who lives in Saint Francisville, Louisiana. She has a BA in political science and a law degree. She stepped away from law in 2006 when her son Billy (now eight years old) was diagnosed with a complex health condition. She quickly jumped online for information and support, never looking back. Catherine loves building and being a part of online and offline communities. She shares her story through her website called "supercatcalhoun" (www.supercatcalhoun.com). She can also be found on twitter as @supercatcalhoun and on Facebook.

To learn more about Catherine's health and rare disease projects, visit:

www.calhounbonepainproject.org

To make a donation to the bone pain research fund, visit:

www.bit.ly/bonepainfund

A Fighting Chance

Research and Community Provide Realistic Hope

by Jordana Holovach

"The internet has made our small disease larger, and we are able to educate so many more people now. Jacob's Cure has received random donations through social media; it has made us so much more visible to people all over the world. I see it as an amazing tool – it has given us a fighting chance."

When I was pregnant with my son, Jacob, in 1995, I insisted on genetic testing. A family friend had a child with a severe genetic disorder and I was horrified by her prognosis and the fact that she was genetically sentenced to death. Thinking that this mother would have to watch her child deteriorate and die touched me deeply. So I wanted to be sure that nothing was wrong with my own pregnancy. At the time, the internet hadn't boomed yet; Google did not exist and information was not as easily accessible, so I put faith in my doctor, who tested me for two disorders based on my ethnic background. Despite passing both tests, I worried throughout my pregnancy.

Midway through my pregnancy, following a sonogram, I was put on bed rest because my amniotic fluid was low. Again I worried and called my doctor, suggesting she forgot to test me for something. She reassured me that everything was fine; I spent the rest of the pregnancy in bed and gave birth to Jacob five weeks early.

When Jacob was five weeks old, after attending Mommy and Me classes, I noticed he wasn't developing like the other babies. The doctors told me to give him time to develop because he was five weeks behind. When he wasn't lifting his head at three months, I knew in my heart something wasn't right. Jacob's pediatrician remained passive. I felt like he thought I was crazy and hormonal. I went to another doctor for a second opinion, and he agreed that something didn't seem right. Together we sought out a neurologist, and after months of tests the doctors believed that Jacob had Lee's Syndrome. When the MRI results came in, the radiologist felt that the diagnosis was incorrect and that perhaps some static event occurred at birth.

As time went on, it was clear Jacob was not developing normally, and additional testing led us to the final diagnosis of Canavan Disease, which we received when he was six months old. Doctors explained to me that Jacob would never sit, crawl, walk, or say a single word. He would live trapped in his body, develop seizures, require a feeding tube, and lose his eyesight. This horrific deterioration is a result of the fact that Canavan prevents the normal formation of white matter that acts as a transmitter of impulses from the brain. Without treatment, death usually occurs by age four.

This information was initially incredibly hard for me to absorb. My body was numb and I was devastated. It was everything I'd feared – my biggest nightmare had come true. For a few weeks, my family and I just sat there in shock and mourned the child we had hoped would live a healthy life. I remember bringing Jacob home after the diagnosis. I was nursing him and was so saddened by the realization that I was nourishing him to die.

The first week hit me the hardest, but I was ready to fight back. After countless sleepless nights, I realized it was time to get motivated. I could not just sit around and watch my child die. I knew my job would be to save his life, no matter what the sacrifice. I told myself, "If it's genetic, we need to fix his genes." The doctors explained that this was an "approachable disease," a disease that could be tackled, but they also told me, "You aren't going to find a team out there, and if you do, it is too rare a disease to warrant significant federal funding." Essentially I was told I would have to do everything on my own.

Amazingly enough, I soon found hope. After

some research I found Dr. Paola Leone, whose team was working on gene therapy for Canavan Disease. One little girl with Canavan who had received the gene therapy in New Zealand was actually able to regenerate some of the white matter or myelin. It was incredible news. One week we were given an unbelievably devastating diagnosis, and then the next week, we discovered a team of researchers working on the disease. It was a rollercoaster of emotion. I wanted to drive to Dr. Leone's office that night and camp out in a sleeping bag outside the front door. I knew I needed to meet her and begin funding her work because Jacob needed treatment quickly. Early the next morning, I connected with Dr. Leone by phone. That call was the starting point of my life; I was ready to fight for a cure for Canavan Disease.

When I contacted Dr. Leone, I learned her team was in the process of closing their doors – they had no money left for research. Thankfully, I was able to immediately send her a check for $250,000 and quickly began raising more with a letter writing campaign that notified our community, friends, and colleagues of Jacob and our fight for his life.

I founded Jacob's Cure in 2000. Over the past 10 years, we have raised nearly 10 million dollars, fought and won approval for two gene therapy trials, and have funded research into pharmacological interventions that have stopped or halted the progression of the disease in all of the treated children. Additionally, the research done in our labs is helping the treatment of other diseases, such as Parkinson's, MS, and ALS. We are currently funding a cutting-edge stem cell trial that aims to further treat or cure Canavan children. Although the estimated research budget for the next three years is a staggering 7 million dollars, we will continue to do whatever it takes to fund this lifesaving work.

Today, Jacob is 14 and is doing quite well. He remains 100 percent dependent, but I believe the gene therapy and pharmaceuticals have kept him strong, healthy, and active. I am thankful we can still smile together, laugh together, and enjoy each other.

Being on the cutting edge of medical research is exciting and hopeful, but it's difficult managing both networking for the cause and caring for a child. As Jacob gets older, new issues arise regarding his care. In one way or another, I am always convincing people he deserves something. I am always advocating. He receives 24/7 care because there are so many things to manage – from his head to his toes. For example, he has medications to take every 20 minutes every single day. We are lucky he has a wonderful team of nurses.

In a recent 24-hour spinal fusion surgery, doctors placed a rod through Jacob's spine. Beforehand, the surgeon explained to me that he had lost some patients as a result of the severity of the surgery, but amazingly, Jacob recovered beautifully and was ready for discharge from the hospital in just a week. I was amazed, but I know he's a fighter. Jacob is an amazing kid who is strong and able to bounce back. He inspires me to get up every day and not complain about anything.

Jacob's nurses and special education teachers have been devoted to him since he was six. They spend every day making sure he is comfortable and stimulated. They treat him with respect and dignity. The other children at his school have been sensitive and interactive; they adore him. It is such a gift for him to be surrounded by children who want to make his life better. Even though he can't talk, he conveys volumes, and people just gravitate toward him. I believe he encourages those around him to be better people by being kind and accepting of others.

The battle for funding and awareness is always uphill; it is always a challenge in one way or another. Accessing funds for such a rare disease is always difficult because it requires being a squeaky wheel at all times. However, parents of children with rare diseases truly have the power to make things happen. We can call politicians, access press contacts, and meet with the decision makers on Capitol Hill. When we stand up and fight for our kids, we can make amazing things happen.

Before the internet, we were alone. In 1996, when Jacob was born, there was no search engine to offer me any information. Today, because of social media, we are connected with many people who are fighting the same fight as we are. The internet has made our small disease larger and we are able to educate many more people now. Jacob's Cure has received random donations through social media; it has made us so much more visible to people all over the world. I see it as an amazing tool – it has given us a fighting chance. This year, because of the connection we have established with so many of the families through email and Facebook, we will be hosting the first ever Canavan Family Conference along with our biennial Research Summit. This will be an opportunity for all the families to meet each other and will hopefully help them feel less alone.

At the end of the day, the work Jacob's Cure has done over the past 10 years has moved us many steps closer towards a cure. When Jacob was diagnosed, there was nothing – no pharmaceutical regimen, no clinical trials, no research towards a cure. Now, our clinical trial could revolutionize the treatment of brain disease. Dr. Leone and the lab we fund inspire me every day. She is devoted and passionate about finding a cure and believes a successful treatment is in the near future. Thank God there is a scientist out there who doesn't just want to publish papers – she wants to help people. I look forward to the day when we do not receive any more emails or calls from devastated parents who have just received a Canavan diagnosis for their child. Until then, Jacob's Cure will be here for them and will continue fighting for a cure.

About the Author

Twelve years ago Jordana Holovach was faced with the horror that her son, Jacob, was born with Canavan Disease, a rare, fatal, genetic brain disease that affects children at birth, robbing them of their ability to sit, crawl, walk, or speak. After coming to terms with the fact that her son would eventually develop seizures, become blind, lose his ability to swallow, and become lost to the world around him, Jordana founded Jacob's Cure for the purpose of treating and ultimately curing Canavan Disease to save her son's life and eradicate the disease.

Since the inception of Jacob's Cure in 2000, the organization has been at the forefront of funding cutting-edge research in the treatment of Canavan, including gene and stem cell therapies. Accomplishments have included two gene-therapy clinical trials, pharmacological interventions, and a research partnership with Geron Corp, which is currently working with the Canavan research team (led by Dr. Paola Leone) on a future stem cell clinical trial in Canavan Disease.

Prior to becoming a mother and fundraiser/ advocate, Jordana worked in the public relations industry and credits those years as a publicist for the success and growth of Jacob's Cure. "Building our donor base and awareness of Jacob's Cure has been solely made possible by our networking and strategic press placements that have opened many doors for us," explains Jordana. "Engaging in collaborative relationships like those involved in the Jewish Genetic Disease Consortium (JGDC) is equally important for rare diseases like Canavan. Our voices are that much louder when we are united."

To learn more about Jacob's Cure or to make a donation, visit:

www.JacobsCure.org

Shared Secrets

The Verbal Shorthand of 'The Sisterhood'

by Janis Marie

"I posed this question to my blog community. 'Do you ever find that typical moms do not understand your special needs lingo?' The consensus seemed to be that those belonging to 'the sisterhood' are comforted in sharing a secret language. We connect. We comfort. We accept each other."

I started writing and sharing my son's journey before he was even born. I started his personal blog when he was 18 months old, not knowing one person outside of my immediate family who knew anything about my son's clinical diagnosis, branchio-oto-renal (BOR) syndrome. I'm happy, ecstatic really, to report that this is no longer the case. Now, as he is turning three years old, our world, our blog, and our community have grown. I know hundreds of families whose children also have a rare disease diagnosis, and some like us, who are still technically undiagnosed. We met online.

Behind, or should I say alongside, every person with a chronic, disabling, or rare disease is a caregiver. Most of us go by a common name: Mom. The internet has facilitated a way for us to connect, meet, and share. Social media has empowered a movement of moms and caregivers to rise up and reach out to one another, not only to ask for help, but to share our stories – sometimes sad, sometimes triumphant, but always REAL.

A few months ago I started contributing to several popular sites for special needs parents. Often times I would sit and stare at my computer waiting for the perfect anecdote to come to mind that others could relate to, and then it would hit me. I wrote the following article about something very small and simple. I found that it really helped so many parents realize that although our kids have varying diagnoses, we have much more in common than we may think. Sometimes it really is the little things that matter most.

Recently it became obvious to me that special needs parents often speak to each other in code. I suppose it has always been around and is often used in medical support forums where everyone is speaking the same lingo.

You know it. It's the shorthand: neuro, pulmo, CHD, mito, OT, PT, and CI, just to name a few. I guess I have been so immersed in what writer and special needs mom Ellen Seidman calls "the sisterhood of the special needs child," I never realized we were speaking a whole different language.

Actually, it is not just special needs parents. Nearly every group has its own lingo: SEO, LOL, DH, FB. Abbreviations are everywhere.

Now granted, not every special needs parent will know and use the same lingo, which is to be expected as not all special needs kids are created equal. What I did not realize is the use of this shorthand was somehow bothersome to others who do not have a child with special needs or background.

Because personal life often spills over onto social media sites like Facebook or Twitter, occasionally someone will use this "special needs lingo." No worries. Those who understand will respond to the question at hand. Generally, those who have no idea what the person is saying will not comment on the particular conversation, or offer some other kind of support. ((HUGS)) are always welcome.

Lately I have noticed quite a few "I have no idea what you mean," "what are you talking about?," "you lost me" type of responses. Huh?

I was interested in what other moms who care for special children had to say about this, so I posed this question to my blog community.

"Do you ever find that typical moms do not understand your special needs lingo?"

I received such honest responses. Without

hesitation, one mother whose child has a rare heart defect answered, "DEFINITELY." She admits to saving such conversation for other special needs moms online, because often she feels like an alien speaking another language with her family.

Ah, people who understand. The consensus seemed to be that those belonging to "the sisterhood" are comforted in sharing a secret language.

We connect. We comfort. We accept each other.

But I think my friend, Barb D., said it best: "Not having to explain terms and language is what makes our bond as mothers of kids with special needs unique. We bring one another comfort simply by knowing what the other is talking about. What a gift!"

I have to agree. It is a gift to be able to connect with and support other special needs parents online, and I plan to keep doing so. That's what I love about this community; someone who understood ME was able to put something that was really bothering me into perspective.

It turns out our language is not so secret after all. It's called support. It is the gift we give to one another.

About the Author

Janis Marie is a full-time mom and freelance writer. Highly regarded and respected for her "tell it like it is" approach, she created and maintains Sneak Peek at Me (www.SneakPeekatMe.com) to chronicle her son's life and medical journey.

Recently highlighted as a featured blogger on Support for Special Needs, she has also written for popular sites, including 5 Minutes for Special Needs, Hopeful Parents, Kidz, Complex Child, RARE Blog (CDRN), and the award winning special needs blog, Love That Max.

Through her blog and affiliations, Janis works year-round to promote awareness and acceptance for those living with a rare disease diagnosis.

She's also a contributing writer to She Posts, where, as a self proclaimed social media junkie, she is free to be a nerd.

To learn more or donate to the Children's Craniofacial Association, visit:

www.CCAkids.com

Mom on a Mission

Overcoming Struggles, Celebrating Milestones

by Laura Buchanan

"As parents of a child with a rare disease, we are her strongest advocates. We are often the ones to educate the doctors on her disorder, fight insurance companies to pay for therapies, and teach the world around us… how prevalent the rare disease community is as a whole."

Three simple words changed our lives:

MOLAR TOOTH SIGN.

Haley is our only child. She was born on Leap Day, unique from the very beginning, without complications. She was a happy and healthy baby. We had no reason to suspect she was anything but perfect. But as weeks turned into months, it became apparent that she was different than other babies. Haley was not doing the normal things that infants her age were doing. She wasn't rolling over, couldn't bounce up and down on my legs, and did not attempt to crawl. She also had some abnormal head movements and looked out of the corners of her eyes a lot. Our pediatrician assured us that she was fine and would catch up by the time she was 18 months old, that most first-time parents over-analyze their baby's behaviors and compare them too closely with their peers.

Shortly after her first Christmas, when she was 10 months old, she could not play with a "stand and cruise" toy she received as a present. She wanted to play with it so badly, but just could not do it. She could only sit there and look at it and cry helplessly. It was heartbreaking, and I had had enough. I took her to the pediatrician and insisted there was something wrong with her. To appease me, he reluctantly referred us to a physical therapist. The PT immediately recognized there was a problem with Haley. She was able to get the ball rolling with multiple therapists and specialists. I credit her with getting us started with finding the help and answers we needed.

The next few months were a whirlwind of doctor visits and therapy sessions. In the meantime, I feverishly scoured the internet looking up Haley's symptoms. I searched day and night for a possible diagnosis. In my research, I encountered many frightening diagnoses, but one disorder stuck with me and I filed it away in my subconscious: Joubert Syndrome, which is a disorder characterized by the "molar tooth sign" on MRI.

Haley had an MRI when she was 13 months old. I received a phone call the same day as her MRI for an appointment to meet with the doctor later that week. I knew then that we finally had an answer to all of our questions.

The neurologist sat down with us and started drawing a picture of a "normal" brain. Then he drew Haley's brain. He was about to say, "This is the molar tooth sign," and I blurted out the phrase at the same time. He looked at me quizzically and asked if I had ever heard of it. He admitted he had not. I wondered how on earth a neurologist could not know about the neurological disorder my daughter had. This was his field of study after all! Little did I know, very few people have ever heard of Joubert Syndrome. Even some neurologists have never heard of it.

Joubert Syndrome most commonly affects a person's gross and fine motor development, balance, coordination, eye movements, breathing patterns, and speech, and also can affect the liver and kidneys. Involvement varies widely from very mild to severe. It is a recessive genetic disorder in which both parents carry the gene. Medical science offers no treatment or cure.

Haley is mildly affected. At 33 months old, she can walk about ten feet independently. She attends a "mainstream" preschool, loves to paint and draw, enjoys music, and is a very happy child. She receives physical therapy twice a week and occupational, speech, play, and visual therapy once a week. She continues to struggle with speech and some sensory issues.

Approximately 350 people in the U.S. and 650 people worldwide are affected by Joubert Syndrome, which classifies it as a rare disease. When Haley was diagnosed, I became a M.O.M., a "mom on a mission." As parents of a child with a rare disease, we are her strongest advocates. We are often the ones to educate the doctors on her disorder, fight insurance companies to pay for therapies, and teach the world around us what Joubert Syndrome is and how prevalent the rare disease community is as a whole. I do not hide Haley's disorder, nor am I ashamed that she has special needs. I find it therapeutic to share our journey and our struggles with others and celebrate the smallest of milestones.

About the Author

Laura Buchanan lives in a small suburb outside of Charlotte, NC with her husband, Will, and her daughter, Haley. Will is a salesperson for a large swimming pool distribution company, and Laura is a home health nurse. They have been married for seven years. Haley is their first child and was born in February 2008. Laura and Will are actively involved in the Joubert Syndrome Foundation; last year they started a fundraising campaign called, "Jog for Joubert Syndrome."

To learn more about Jog for Joubert Syndrome, or to donate, visit:

www.jogforjoubertsyndrome.blogspot.com

Racing the Clock

Leveraging the Power of the Internet to Find a Cure

by Matt and Lori Sames

"The web gave us the ability to reach out globally and has allowed us to find a community... We now have gene delivery treatment, and we are working to fund research for clinical trials on safety and efficacy. We've been working at warp speed toward establishing a clinical trial to treat children with GAN. It's powerful to bring people together to collaborate and brainstorm."

Lori

Hannah is a beautiful little girl with curly blonde hair. She has a beautiful heart. The effect she has on people is like magic. As a baby, Hannah met all her infant milestones. But when she was two years and five months old, her Grammy noticed her left arch seemed to be rolling inward. We decided to take Hannah to an orthopedist and a podiatrist, but we were assured she would be fine.

At three years old, both of her arches were rolling and her gait had become awkward, and we were worried. We were referred to a pediatric neurologist. Hannah went through six months of testing with a pediatric geneticist, but all the results came back normal.

Then on March 24, 2008, we learned that Hannah has Giant Axonal Neuropathy (GAN). It impacts every nerve cell in the body, slowly progressing as the central nervous system becomes involved. We didn't realize exactly how grim the diagnosis was until we met with our genetic counselor three days later. I looked at her and asked, "So you're telling us that this is a death sentence?" She said, "Yes." It was the single most devastating moment of our lives.

And then Matt just looked at me and said, "You know someone has to be the first. Someone has to be the first to be cured."

Matt

GAN is an orphan disease. There's no funding, no research, no support group. The patients don't know where the other patients are. People can't talk about this with anyone. Neurologists who practice for 30 years never see patients who have this. The doctors give you the death sentence and then you have to learn to cope. And we just can't accept that.

Lori

When Hannah's diagnosis hit us, we were baffled that there were ravaging disorders out there with no treatment options. As of January 2009, out of the 43 disorders under the Muscular Dystrophy Association umbrella, only one genetic disorder has an FDA approved treatment – it's for Pompe Disease. We learned it was actually the family that paved the way and developed the treatment that saved their children. For these orphan diseases, the families have to get the treatment developed. That was the most surprising and devastating realization.

Matt

Lori immediately dove into any information she could find, but I was paralyzed for three days. Then we both put our heads together, and she took over the medical research and I took on the fundraising/marketing management side.

Lori

Without the internet, we'd be at sqaure one. After Hannah's diagnosis, I was researching on the web nearly 24 hours a day for eight weeks. It allowed us to quickly reach scientists all over the world who were studying GAN. It wasn't being researched in the U.S. when Hannah was diagnosed. The web gave us the ability to reach out globally and has allowed us to find a community. GAN is very rare. We keep in close contact with other families in the U.S. and in Belgium. These families contacted us through our website, but we also communicate with them using Facebook.

Matt

We had to create all of this. There was no research and no foundation. In the past, individual researchers would do a project, publish a paper, and then move on. We contacted all those researchers and invited them to a symposium to discuss GAN in 2008. Twenty-two scientists participated, and it was the first time GAN had been discussed. Out of that meeting, the consensus was to develop a gene delivery.

Lori

On the scientific front, we quickly realized that we may be able to find treatments for other disorders as we pursue a treatment for GAN. Dr. Jude Samulski at Chapel Hill sent an associate to the symposium to learn about the disorder and assess whether there was a possibility for gene therapy delivery. We now have gene delivery treatment, and we are working to fund research for clinical trials on safety and efficacy. We've been working at warp speed toward establishing a clinical trial to treat children with GAN. It's powerful to bring people together to collaborate and brainstorm.

Matt

We are racing against the clock here. We'd like to begin human trials as early as nine months from now. It could be so exciting for us and other families. Our research could translate to other diseases. The effect could be so profound. It's human nature for researchers to go about their business, but we see our daughter falling and failing and we have a sense of urgency that the researchers will never have. We don't have meetings to make decisions. We just say "go."

Lori

Hannah has played T-ball for the last two springs. She tries to run and falls, but always gets back up. We hold her hand and walk the bases with her. Her ability to walk is becoming impaired.

Matt

Hannah never complains, though. It was hard emotionally to watch Hannah play T-ball because she can't run. She would hit the ball, I would grab her hand, and we would walk to first base. She gave it 110 percent.

She likes to dance. Sometimes she has trouble controlling her balance. During the recital, she was very close to the edge of the stage and Lori and I were so nervous. But she did great and marched off the stage with the other little girls.

Lori

Hannah keeps me strong in my most difficult moments. If I've been away from her for a few hours or if we've hit a road block in a study, once I'm home and around Hannah, she is full of love and happiness and it keeps me strong. Hannah is our youngest. She's in first grade, but she has an old soul. It's bittersweet. The bitter is obvious. The sweet is that our family can really live in the moment and focus on building lasting memories.

Matt

My wife keeps me strong in the most difficult moments. She's so determined and strong; it gives me inspiration. My daughters inspire me. They go out of their way to help Hannah. And Hannah never complains. If I'm ever feeling sorry for myself, all I have to do is remember that she never complains.

About the Authors

Lori Sames is a homemaker and the Executive Director of Hannah's Hope Fund. Matt Sames is the Managing Partner of Pet Lodges, Inc. and Checkerhills Farm. He has worked in advertising sales and management at television stations.

Matt and Lori are the parents of three beautiful girls. Their youngest, Hannah, was diagnosed with Giant Axonal Neuropathy (GAN), a rare genetic disorder, in 2008. At that time there was no treatment or foundation for GAN. Lori and Matt created Hannah's Hope Fund to connect with researchers and families around the world to raise awareness and funds for a treatment of GAN. Hannah's Hope Fund now has a gene delivery treatment, and is working to fund research for clinical trials on safety and efficacy to treat children with GAN.

To learn more about Hannah's Hope Fund or donate, visit:

www.hannahshopefund.org

A Parent's Promise

Learning, Training Enable Independent Care

by Julie Loeffler

"We're doing everything I promised our sweet little boy when he was first born. I was worried when he was first diagnosed, but with education, determination, and a lot of support from each other, Keith and I are giving Kyler the most normal life he could have."

From the moment I saw Kyler, I knew my life had changed for the better. I couldn't stop kissing his sweet little head when the doctor handed him to me. He is and always will be my living angel.

The emotions and feelings of overwhelming love and satisfaction for a new mom are amazing. Sure, I was tired. Sure, I needed to recover from my c-section, but all I wanted to do was hold my brand new baby boy and tell him how much I loved him and how happy I was to finally meet him. I told him I was going to protect him and if he ever needed anything, I would be there for him.

Little did I know that just over 24 hours later, he would be transferred to Children's Memorial Hospital in Chicago, 45 minutes away from our hospital in a suburb. Kyler was circumcised and the incision wouldn't clot. His blood saturated diapers. The pediatrician and my OB were worried.

Kyler was literally taken out of my arms, and I watched him get rolled away in an incubator. My husband Keith kissed me and then left to be with Kyler in Chicago. I wasn't able to leave the hospital until I recovered. I anxiously awaited updates from Keith. When they finally came, we were told that Kyler has hemophilia type A, severe. I knew hemophilia had to do with blood, but that was pretty much it.

Once I was finally released, Keith drove me to Children's. When we got there, my sweet little boy was laying in the crib, looking up at me. To this day I think he was relieved when he saw me. I scooped him up and told him we'd do everything in our power to give him as normal of a life as possible.

Throughout the next couple of days, we met with nurses and doctors. Keith paid attention, but I honestly had a hard time listening. I just wanted to be with my baby, and I was exhausted from barely sleeping for the past few days. We were told about types of bleeds and someday treating him at home. We were told about factor replacement therapy and inhibitors. It all went in one ear and out the other. I was in denial. I went through every emotion in the book: anger, denial, fear, sadness, guilt, frustration. You name it, I went through it. I was scared. I was the person who had to sit by the window during dissection in school. The sight of blood and needles makes me faint, and now my child has a bleeding disorder. How in the world was I going to do everything he needed me to do?

It took me a couple of months to really learn about hemophilia. I had to do it when I was ready.

At first I would pick up the books, read a few pages, and start crying. Keith dove right into the plethora of books, pamphlets, and information that were given to us at Children's. I caught up as I got stronger. Once I started learning, I didn't stop. I told that little boy when he was born that I would do anything I could to protect him, and I was determined to keep my promise.

I've been a member of one particular online community for a number of years. This group of women and a few men have seen me get married, supported me through my pregnancy, and have been wonderful sources of encouragement through all of Kyler's hemophilia issues. Whenever Kyler would have a bleed in the beginning, they were always good listeners and encouraged me to keep learning and doing what we were doing. Now that we know more, they've encouraged me to get our story out to the hemophilia community and to share the knowledge that I have gained in the past couple of years. I have also met other hemophilia moms online through my blog and through hemophilia groups who have helped assure me that my emotions and feelings are completely normal.

Kyler has since had a number of bleeds. The first few were tough, but we learned from them. Going to the hospital hoping the nursing staff would be able to find a vein on a chubby, wiggly little baby was extremely frustrating. We learned that we are Kyler's voice. We are the ones who have to say "no" when doctors or nurses want to do something we don't approve of. Since hemophilia is such a rare disorder, most medical professionals in emergency rooms don't know much about it. I've had to tell an ER doctor "no" when he wanted to access the vein in Kyler's head. We were at the hospital because he hit his head really hard on a corner in our kitchen. The rule is that you don't touch the area that is injured. From past experience, I learned that the vein on the top of his right foot is pretty good and had the most success. I insisted they use that vein. They listened and Kyler had his factor moments later.

Kyler now has a port. We pleaded our case to get one after he had his first joint bleed in his ankle.

Joint bleeds can be scary. If they're not treated completely, permanent damage can occur. Usually joint bleeds need to be treated at least two to three times before they're completely healed. We didn't want to put Kyler through multiple hospital trips with multiple pokes if we didn't have to. The port was our best option. When we were pushing for Kyler's port, other moms in the online hemophilia community encouraged me to pursue it. They told us their success stories and said that we would have a whole new perspective on Kyler's disorder once the port was placed. Ever since Kyler got his port at 14-½ months, we haven't had to worry about ER trips and nurses accessing a vein. We don't have to worry about six, seven, even eight pokes and a dehydrated kid from crying from all the needle sticks. We still go to the hospital if Kyler's injury needs to be x-rayed or he needs to get checked out by a doctor.

We learned how to access Kyler's port from home care nurses. They came once a week for about an hour for two months. Usually people learn how to access the port at a Hemophilia Treatment Center (HTC) from the hemophilia nurse. Since we live so far away from our HTC, the home care nurses were our best option. After our training, Keith and I decided that we are the only ones who are allowed to access Kyler's port. We trust each other and know we're doing all the steps we were taught. Kyler helps out with his infusions too. He points to his port and tells us that is where factor goes. He's a smart little boy. He tells us when he has an owie and shows us where it hurts. The port has taught us all valuable lessons!

We have become stronger, more confident, and more determined since Kyler had his port surgery. Bleeds aren't as big of a deal as they once were. Currently Kyler is getting infusions twice a week as prophylaxis. It's going well. Keith and I take turns doing Kyler's infusions. If we are ever in a situation where the other person isn't there, we're 100% confident we could give Kyler the medication he needs as soon as possible. Situations have come up where I've had to leave work to treat

Kyler or Keith was out of town on business when Kyler had a bleed. It's not always easy in different settings, but it's possible and we've always persevered.

Kyler is happy, energetic, playful, and he acts like any other 2 ½ year-old! We make sure he's treated like any other toddler would be treated. He's taken swimming lessons, jumps in bounce houses, runs across playgrounds, and plays games with all of his friends who don't have a bleeding disorder! We haven't met a kid who hasn't had something to worry about. Whether it's a food allergy, diabetes, a learning disability, etc., it seems like every kid has something that isn't perfect. Hemophilia just happens to be our "blip" on Kyler's radar.

We're doing everything I promised our sweet little boy when he was first born. I was worried when he was first diagnosed, but with education, determination, and a lot of support from each other, Keith and I are giving Kyler the most normal life he could have.

About the Author

Julie Loeffler lives in Gurnee, IL with her husband, Keith, and two-year-old son, Kyler. Kyler was born with hemophilia type A, severe. Julie and Keith continue to educate themselves and others on Kyler's disorder. Julie has recently become involved in the hemophilia community. She was the Team Captain of Kyler's Krew for the 1st annual Hemophilia Walk in Illinois. She also enjoys speaking to new moms of sons with bleeding disorders. She answers questions and concerns they may have, as well as gives advice when needed. She has been given an enormous amount of support and encouragement from other moms in the community, and hopes to pass the same support on to others.

To learn more about Julie, Keith, and Kyler, visit:

www.kylerbean.blogspot.com

To learn more or donate to Hemophilia Foundation of Illinois, visit:

www.hemophiliaillinois.org

Beyond Coping

Finding Strength in Shared Adversity

by Terri Granard

"I talk with people from all over the world – and I use Google Translator a lot! It's about giving people hope, even if it's a shot in the dark... You have to look to other parents, and you have to be there for each other."

I have a son named Eli. He has Ring 14 Deletion, a chromosomal abnormality that "just happened" during normal cell division. It's so rare there are only 300 documented cases in the world.

Eli is one of two beautiful stars in our sky. The other is his big brother, Noah, who is one year older, intelligent, articulate, and with no medical issues at all.

Because of his genetic abnormality, Eli has developmental delays (he functions at a two-year-old level even though he's ten), daily seizures, respiratory trouble that requires frequent CPR, numerous strokes, feeding issues – the works. He has a very fragile immune system and gets pneumonia and croup if the wind blows the wrong way. His story is one of love, hope, faith, endurance, and constant worry for those who love him.

Eli was born perfect. He was a beautiful boy with no known health problems except he showed no head growth at his five-month checkup. At the time, we were told, "Don't worry, he will catch up." Then at six months, he had a series of seizures. He was gasping, jerking, staring, having tremors, unresponsive to our voices, limp, and had dilated pupils.

We took him to the hospital for myriad tests. He was observed, poked, scanned, and measured. Everything possible was done for him. He was sent home with a diagnosis of idiopathic epilepsy, seizures of unknown origin. We had to wait for his chromosome analysis, which was expected to be normal. But when the test results came back from Duke University three weeks later, 20 out of 20 cells tested were affected by Ring 14.

We made more appointments and scanned the internet. What we found was heartbreaking. Barely anything existed to help us find answers, except a few examples of very sickly looking infants that didn't look like Eli. We were lucky to find some support groups. This is where we began to learn about our son, through other parents who have children with similar illnesses.

Of course, we were devastated by all of this. We weren't prepared to live a life of 24-hour care for our baby. Our living room turned in an intensive care unit. What about his brother? What about normal family life? We were never told about resources, equipment needed, and the many hours of worry.

Eli requires 24/7 care and on a daily basis is dependent on anti-convulsant therapy and his vagus nerve stimulator. He also has a g-tube placed in his stomach. He eats mostly through this tube, but can tolerate small amounts of water and food orally.

The good news is that he's generally not in any pain and has little understanding of his situation (we think). Eli's always happy when not enduring the effects of a seizure, and the joy he brings us as parents is immense. It has been a blessing having Eli in our lives and we hope he continues to thrive in his own way. While we've had to drastically adapt our lives around his needs, we've also been blessed with the challenges and love that raising such a child brings to your life.

As a mom, I always feel like I'm spreading myself too thin. For Eli alone in 2009, we had 65 doctor appointments, five hospitalizations, 130 prescription refills, two emergency room visits, a half-dozen different nurses in-home, one birthday party to attend, and endless telephone conversations with all of his "people," from doctors to priests and rabbis.

I also have multiple sclerosis, so I have the good fortune of not remembering half of what has happened, and not remembering what I told to whom.

I know I am tired for a reason, but I wouldn't change it for a second if it meant not having Eli, Noah, or my wonderful husband, Ryan. My family has taught me that they are always number one.

I have made the best friends in the world because of Eli. I have lost some too. Older friends have stayed true, and others fell to the wayside.

Some of my closest relationships are with people we've met online. Eli and I have flown from Los Angeles to Tennessee twice to visit a family that has a child with Ring 14. It's like meeting someone who has not only the same blood type you do, but the same fingerprints.

Because I'm on the outreach registry of an organization called Unique, The Rare Chromosome Disorder Support Group (www.rarechromo.org), I've met with 20 parents in the last 10 years. As a spokesperson, I've been able to share with other families the things we've worked out with our doctors that are keeping Eli alive, such as a vagus nerve stimulator that reduced his seizures from 80 to eight, and a feeding tube which means he doesn't have to be in the hospital all the time with an IV. I was able to tell these parents how Ring 14 affects your immune system, and that during seizures their child may stop breathing, so they'll need to have some form of CPR available. No doctor in the world will know this, because there's almost nothing in the medical literature about this condition.

I talk with people from all over the world – and I use Google Translator a lot! It's about giving people hope, even if it's a shot in the dark. There are advances in medicine every day. That's why Eli is alive. You have to look to other parents, and you have to be there for each other.

Eli was made this way for a specific reason. His pain and agony I don't understand. Why do babies have to suffer so? His disease, this specific disease, Ring 14, I understand. I only hope I meet more people who can hold me up as I get older.

We have been blessed to have Eli in our lives. He is a pure soul and really a fun little guy. We can't imagine life without him. He has a "presence" in everyone's eyes. I can't say enough about how he draws people to him, as does his big brother.

God bless all us parents. No one knows what we go through in 24 hours with our angels. Remember, though, it's worth it. But you knew that.

About the Author

Terri Granard lives in Southern California with her husband and two young sons. Since her son Eli's diagnosis with a rare chromosomal disease called Ring 14, she has been an advocate and supporter of those affected with similar issues.

Terri's motto is: "Where there is great love, there are miracles."

To learn more about Terri and Eli, visit:

www.ring14.net

To learn more about medical research for Ring 14 or donate, visit:

www.ring14.org

Purpose in Pain

Perseverance is its Own Reward

by Dominique Friend

"Rare disease patients breathe inspiration into my life and continually give me hope to do more. When I read positive comments about how I've made a difference in another patient's life, it sticks with me and buoys me up. When I feel like I can't fight another day, someone will send me an encouraging message and it will inspire me to keep going."

Being both a parent and a patient has its challenges. I have three kids, ages 25, 19, and 14; two step kids, ages 25 and 29; and a five-year-old granddaughter. I also have sickle cell, a rare disorder which I've nicknamed Sickle Mom Syndrome.

Every day I deal with chronic pain because of the abnormal shaped blood cells in my body. It is a pain worse than childbirth – a pain I've experienced all my life.

Chronic pain makes it hard for me to function as a normal mom. The pain affects my ability to do simple things like cook dinner on a regular basis or attend football games, because I tire easily. I have trouble standing for long periods of time. Every day is a challenge to keep up with my life's activities. Simple activities like going shopping with my daughter or doing a load of laundry can be so draining for me.

Despite all of the challenges we face as a family, I know my kids are proud of me. I've taught them this lesson in perseverance: no matter what you go through in life, you'll always have obstacles to overcome.

I've certainly had my share of obstacles along the way. Sickle cell patients generally only live to their early forties. For a while, my son wasn't doing well in school, and when I talked to him about it, he said, "I can't concentrate because I'm worried about how much longer you'll be here, Mom." This was a very hard conversation to have, but we needed to address the issue. My husband and I encourage open communication, which means our family always talks, no matter how painful it may be. We have a very strong bond as a family, and we get our strength through our faith. Every day I pray to God I'll be able to continue to live my life – even if it's not a life without pain.

Trying to clear up the misconceptions about my disorder presents another challenge. I call sickle cell an invisible disease. On the outside I appear to be perfectly normal and healthy, but on the inside I am in pain for most of the day. Throughout my life, I've found people are quick to judge based on outward appearances, and I've heard, "But you don't look sick," more times than I can count. I have tried to overcome this obstacle by raising awareness for sickle cell.

I have even published my memoirs, *Sickle: a Personal Story of Pain, Purpose, and Perseverance*, as a way of explaining to caregivers, medical professionals, and the public how deeply this invisible disease has affected my life and the lives of others with sickle cell disease. It was not easy to share intimate details of my life with the world, but getting this message out loud and clear seems much more important to me than closely guarding my privacy. At every opportunity, I want to put my story forward, giving others a chance to "walk in my shoes" and understand why those of us with sickle cell disease are looking for both their empathy and their support of our advocacy.

I believe we all have a purpose. Sometimes it takes a difficult situation to help you find your purpose. Your purpose may not be exactly what you want to it be, but I think it's something that God gives all of us. My diagnosis allowed me to find my purpose. I know I want to share my life and let people know that if I can make my way despite this disease, so can they.

I've been an introvert my whole life. I've always been shy, I don't like to be in crowds, and I've always been terrified of public speaking. My purpose changed things. Over the last three years, I've been a guest speaker many times. I realized that my fears didn't matter if I had the opportunity to share my life and create a better understanding of sickle cell. I was shaking before I spoke for the first time, but once I got up there, I felt right where I belonged. After my first speech, several audience members stood up and shared stories about their own disorders. I saw how overcoming my fear helped others break the silence, and in order to create a positive change for the rare disease community, that is exactly what we need to do.

Despite all of the pain, my family, my faith, and my purpose keep me strong. Although it isn't easy to be a patient and a mom, my family is a blessing to me. They give me hope to live. Five years ago, when I become a grandmother, I was going through a hard time with my disease, and then Madison came and gave me yet another reason to fight. Even on the days when I'm really sick, I try to stay focused by telling myself, "You can do this, just send one more email, make one more phone call." My goal is to raise enough awareness of sickle cell that one day others like me will be able to go to any hospital and the staff will be knowledgeable and understanding of the disease.

Other rare disease patients breathe inspiration into my life and continually give me the desire to do more. When I read positive comments about how I've made a difference in another patient's life, it sticks with me and buoys me up. When I feel like I can't fight another day, someone will send me an encouraging message and it will inspire me to keep going.

Now is the time for rare disease patients to become their own advocates. Develop a strategy, think about where you want to see progress in fighting the disease in the next 15-20 years, and then come up with goals to break through to even bigger goals. The internet is a powerful tool in the rare disease community; we have the ability to connect with others all over the world. It is important for us to share our stories because there really is somebody else out there, even when you think you are alone. Lastly, it's important to persevere, no matter what. Don't give up. Things will not come easy. Things will be difficult, but you'll be surprised how much of a difference we can make.

About the Author

Dominique Friend is an advocate for sickle cell disease awareness and research who currently resides in South Central Pennsylvania. She is a wife, the mother of five wonderful children, and has one beautiful granddaughter. Although her illness prevented her from graduating high school, she obtained her GED and then completed post-secondary courses in Creative Writing. Now a published author, Dominique has captured the essence of her daily struggles with the unpredictability and pain of sickle cell disease in her autobiography, *Sickle: A Story of Pain, Purpose, and Perseverance.*

Dominique has become an activist who is raising awareness and advocating for improved treatment for people living with sickle cell disease. She is the founder of the Sickle Cell Encouragement Group, a support group in her local community, and she organized the first Sickle Cell Gala in York,

Pennsylvania, generating funds to assist sickle cell sufferers who are burdened by the expense of travel to obtain specialized medical care.

Dominique's outreach goes as far as Africa and other parts of the world. She has been invited to participate in conferences sponsored by the National Institute of Health and she most recently visited the White House and met with the President's Special Assistant on policies and disabilities, Mr. Kareem Dale. Dominique is also the founder of the newly formed Sickle International Family Coalition, which will be the voice of millions of families throughout the world of sickle cell disease. Dominique can be contacted by telephone at (717) 793-6294 or by email at sickle1000@yahoo.com.

To learn more or donate to Sickle Cell Disease Association of America, visit:

www.sicklecelldisease.org

Life After Life

Grey's Gift Spotlights Need for Rare Disease Screening

by Bill and Nicole Morris

"In the two years since Grey's loss, my family has established his foundation, Grey's Gift, with a mission to educate others of the importance of newborn screening. Grey's gifts are many, but his greatest gift will be saving thousands of little ones from death or disability."

On June 14, 1999, our second son, Seth, was born. Being a few weeks early, he was immediately taken by the nurses for closer inspection, only to be returned a few hours later, the perfect little man we envisioned. We went home from the hospital the next day, and our life with a newborn went on as planned...until day eleven.

On day eleven, our whole world crumbled. A

call from Seth's pediatrician indicated that his newborn screening test came back positive for Phenylketonuria (PKU). Being two educated people – I'm a special education teacher and my husband is a pediatric nurse – we were baffled by our ignorance of this rare disorder.

PKU is a rare condition in which a baby is born without the ability to properly break down an amino acid called phenylalanine. PKU is treatable, but if proteins containing phenylalanine are not avoided, the disorder can lead to mental retardation by the end of the first year of life.

Luckily, PKU is an extremely manageable disorder when identified early, as in Seth's case. We were promised by his metabolic doctor that a change in Seth's diet would allow him to grow into a strong, healthy, intelligent boy. Monitoring his blood levels would ensure that. At the time, Seth's PKU seemed to rock our whole world, but it would eventually prove to be only a bump in the road in this earthquake that would soon shake our lives.

Four years after the birth of our third son, Riley,

our fourth son was born. Greyson came into this world as quietly as could be, barely a peep out of him. As the nurses laid him upon me, I looked into his enormous brown eyes and saw an old, wise soul. We took Grey home, and life with four boys, now ranging from our newest addition to our 13-year-old, became as hectic as one might imagine. Grey took everything in stride, learning to make his needs known and his voice heard.

Outside of a milk allergy, Greyson grew and developed right on schedule. His head control was not great, but he was getting stronger and we were told not to worry, considering his head was a bit larger than normal. I imagine that it was around six months that we noticed something just wasn't right, and we made mention of it at his wellness checkup.

At six months, Grey still had poor head control, but he was very social. He hated to be on his stomach and would scream when you placed him on it. He was starting to roll over but had no interest in sitting. He was perfectly content to lie in his bouncy chair all day and watch the world go round. Due to his birth order and laid-back attitude, we were told that Grey was probably just a "lazy baby." Denial is a powerful thing; these comments were much easier to accept than the doubts my husband and I both had in our hearts.

At eight months, when Grey's skills seemed to be regressing, we scheduled our wellness appointment early. In a matter of just two months, Grey went from rolling over to barely being able to raise his arms. Immediate blood work resulted in a quickly scheduled appointment with a neurologist.

Because Grey was still a social baby, our neurologist was not very concerned with his condition at first. The initial MRI came back clear. A muscle biopsy showed that his muscles were working just fine. However, a nerve conduction test showed that Grey's nerves were not responding as they should have been. At this point, at least, we knew where to start.

Within a month, we were back at the neurologist's office, our son merely a shell of what he had been. Upon seeing Grey, our neurologist admitted him for "failure to thrive," and more testing began. Another MRI indicated deterioration of white matter and a spinal tap revealed our greatest fear: Grey was thought to have some form of leukodystrophy, although we were not sure which one. We were told that his condition was most likely terminal. It was October 31. We discharged him, dressed him up as a giraffe, and took him Trick-or-Treating. Grey gave no indication as to how sick he really was, and our son had the time of his life.

Thanksgiving approached and Grey's little body became more and more like a rag doll. Still very social, eating and drinking on his own, saying "mama" and "dada," his mind perfectly intact, we could see his frustration building as he longed to do the things his body would no longer allow him to do. On the day before Thanksgiving, our neurologist called with a diagnosis for Krabbe Disease.

Krabbe Disease is a rare, inherited degenerative

disorder of the central and peripheral nervous systems. It is characterized by the presence of globoid cells (cells that have more than one nucleus), the breakdown of the nerve's protective myelin coating, and destruction of brain cells. Krabbe Disease is one of a group of genetic disorders called the leukodystrophies. These disorders impair the growth or development of the myelin sheath, the fatty covering that acts as an insulator around nerve fibers, and cause severe degeneration of mental and motor skills. Myelin, which lends its color to the "white matter" of the brain, is a complex substance made up of at least 10 different enzymes. Krabbe Disease is caused by a deficiency of galactocerebrosidase, an essential enzyme for myelin metabolism. The disease most often affects infants, with onset before six months of age and resulting in death before the age of two.

In November we were still looking for a cure. On December 4, after another appointment with our neurologist, we called hospice and took Grey home. It all happened so quickly.

Realizing that Grey would most likely not make it through the holidays, we pulled the boys out of school and spent the next two weeks as a family, drinking in every ounce of Grey that we could. Explaining Grey's outcome to the boys was a task that no parent should ever have to speak and that no child should ever have to hear. Sadly, in the little research we were able to find about Krabbe, we learned that if Grey had been screened for Krabbe at birth, we would have had options, not curable options, but treatable options. It didn't take long for Seth, now 10, to put the pieces together.

"Why me?" he asked. "Why is my disease so much more important than my brother's? Why is my disease screened for and his isn't?"

As a parent, how do you answer that? How do you look into your children's eyes and tell them that, sometimes, life just isn't fair? This was the beginning of our quest for newborn screening equality.

Grey left his broken body on December 12, 2008, six days shy of his first birthday.

In February, we found ourselves meeting with Texas legislators penning a bill to increase the number of diseases screened for in Texas. Emotionally spent, the process was taxing on all of us. We spoke in front of committee members and legislators, sharing our story with anyone who would listen. We used the internet, not only to educate ourselves, but to educate others on the need for expanded newborn screening. Education was the key. It wasn't that people didn't want to expand newborn screening. It was that people didn't even know what newborn screening was.

On June 19, 2009, Governor Rick Perry signed HB 1795, establishing Greyson's Law. Under Greyson's Law, the state was to pay for reprogramming the Tandem Mass Spectrometry machines, expanding screening to a total of 52 disorders compared to the previous 27 disorders. It also was to provide training for state lab employees. It would educate doctors and nurses throughout the state about the additions to the screening program and the disorders added. The

Department of Health would also use some of the funds to ensure comprehensive case management, so each positive-testing child receives all care and treatment necessary to promote the best quality of life possible based on the diagnosis. Unfortunately, our budget was cut, and although we have had success in adding Cystic Fibrosis screening, no other disorders have been added since.

We were, however, able to fund the Newborn Screening Advisory Committee. Greyson's Law created this committee, which is made up of specialists in newborn screening, parents of affected children, representatives from the state lab, and the Texas Hospital Association. The committee assesses and makes recommendations for additions to the screening program to keep Texas proactive in the protection of its infants. I am proud to say that my husband, Bill, was elected chairman of the committee and will serve a six-year term.

New technologies and testing procedures are being developed every day. It is very important that these new methods and technologies be assessed and vetted to determine which will make the best use of state resources in adding diseases to the newborn screening program. It is our hope that the Newborn Screening Advisory Committee will add screening for the disease that took our son's life. The Committee is currently in the process of obtaining $1.8 million through this year's legislative session to completely fund Greyson's Law.

In the two years since Grey's loss, my family has established his foundation, Grey's Gift, with a mission to educate others of the importance of newborn screening. Grey's gifts are many, but his greatest gift will be saving thousands of little ones from death or disability, estimated by the Department of Health to affect upward of 1,500 babies per year.

Greyson was an amazing little boy, doing more in his 11 months than I will ever do in this lifetime. But Grey's greatest gift to me was being the only one in this whole world that he called "mama."

About the Authors

Nicole Morris is the Special Education Department Head at Church Hill Middle School in New Braunfels, Texas, where she has been teaching since 2000. Nicole uses her love of computers to continue to educate others of newborn screening through websites and social media and was essential in spreading awareness throughout Texas' 81st legislative session to help pass Greyson's Law.

Bill Morris has been a pediatric home health nurse since 1996, serving the New Braunfels, Sequin, and San Antonio, Texas areas. He is currently serving a two-year term as the first chairman of Texas' Newborn Screening Advisory Committee, established through Greyson's Law. Bill is instrumental in teaching his community, including expecting parents, new parents, and the medical community, the importance of newborn screening.

To read more about Grey, visit:

www.greysgift.com

To make a donation to Grey's Gift Memorial Foundation, visit:

www.greysgift.org

Grace for Today

Getting Through the Here-and-Now with Hope for Tomorrow

by Joan Bellontine

"Needless to say, I have been 'Graced.' I have a precious and very special life and I am very thankful for it. We are all here temporarily… I have been given the gift of intense realization of this fact so I appreciate special moments more than most people do."

On February 3, 2005, my then 4½-year-old daughter, Grace, was diagnosed with Sanfilippo Syndrome. This rare genetic disease is caused by a missing enzyme. Instead of cells being regenerated, they are stored in the body. This build up causes progressive and degenerative damage to the brain and central nervous system. There is currently no treatment or cure available. In many ways, it is like

Alzheimer's in children, and patients slowly regress and pass away somewhere between the ages of 10 and 30.

The first thought I had after hearing the unbearable news was, "There goes this life – it's over." I remember thinking, "How could I ever sit by and watch this sweet, adorable, wonderful child get sick and die? My sweet baby Grace – my angel!" I have never even remotely considered suicide, but at that moment I couldn't help thinking of any alternative that could take me away from the hell I was experiencing – and the hell I knew I'd have to experience for years to come. As excruciating and intense as the pain was, it actually got worse when I realized, "I can't escape this! I have Julia (my other daughter who is two years older than Grace). My family needs me!" As petrified as I was, I knew that I had to somehow get through this for them.

Grace has cognitive issues and so she was (and still is) completely unaware of what's going on, and Julia is a very bright, vibrant, healthy child.

How was I going to be the exceptional parent I had planned to be to these children who had needs that were so radically different? How could I ever communicate to Julia that she was going to lose her sister? Would I be living in darkness and fear every day for the rest of my life? I was a changed person and I couldn't believe that God didn't love me anymore. What did I do to deserve this? Would I – the one voted "most cheerful" in high school, the person who was always full of optimism and hope – ever smile again? It was all gone, in an instant.

I don't know what carried me through those horrific days as I walked in and out of hospitals and doctors' offices with Grace contently cuddled in her stroller, completely unaware of what was going on. My insides were knotted up with uncertainty and fear. Sometimes at night I would sit next to her bed and just listen to her breathing. In her presence, I felt safer.

Grace has never put two words together with her voice, but her eyes have communicated more than a “typical” person could express in several lifetimes. Her calmness held me together, and as much as I was afraid that God wasn’t listening to me anymore, I somehow summoned a quiet, desperate prayer for mercy. “God, please have mercy on Grace.”

The next day at the breakfast table, Julia told me that she had written a new song and it was called “Have Mercy.” When she sang it to me, tears welled up in my eyes and I wondered if there could be an ounce of hope left for me and my family in this life. Those shimmers of light that managed to peek their way through small cracks in the darkness were the things that kept me going through those times. The next night while again worrying in bed, a very loud message came to me: “Angels will come.”

Slowly, I started to see more and more of those dancing light shafts poking through things, and the first spatters of “angelic intervention” began to arrive at my doorstep. I started to realize the tremendous goodness of mankind and was intrigued to see that I now had a “bird’s-eye” view into humanity that most people do not ever have the privilege to witness.

One day I said to myself, "Maybe everything I am, everyone I know, every experience I have ever had has been preparing me for this! Maybe I was chosen by Grace for this challenge; after all, she needed a mother! Maybe she has a mission here and I am going to help her carry it out!" Slowly I came to grips with these ideas and Grace's "teachings" set my crooked path straight. Her first class was "Living in the Moment 101." This child never thinks about anything other than what is happening in the here and now. This is one of the most important lessons we can learn as human beings. I now live for today more than ever and don't think too much about what tomorrow may or may not bring.

I have also grown to love and respect individuals with special needs and realize the huge importance of their presence here on earth. They are incredibly strong, bring out intense joy in those around them, and are undeniably real. Grace and others like her are explicitly in touch with the most important aspects of life and are, in many ways, happier and better off than most of us! They teach us all about compassion and bring a whole world of supportive professional people together, which astounds me to this day. I am deeply appreciative of the teachers, therapists, administrators, caretakers, nurses, and doctors who have walked this walk with me. Their sacrifice and commitment to these children is one of the most beautiful things I have ever witnessed in my life.

Before this experience, I always felt I had an important purpose and was frustrated about being unable to find it. I tried several ventures, but nothing ever seemed right. I now have a 501c3 not-for-profit organization called "Grace for a Cure, Inc." and hold fundraisers to generate funds towards a cure. I support The Children's Medical Research Foundation, the MPS Society, and have recently become the director of public relations for an organization called Team Sanfilippo. We are all parents on a mission to find a cure or treatment as fast as possible for our children. Facebook has helped us to connect and unite in our mission. I recently heard that we are in the process of applying for approval for a human clinical trial for a treatment for Sanfilippo Syndrome. We need to raise one million dollars as soon as possible. Other parents before us have found treatments for their children with other forms of related disorders, and we are hoping it is now our turn for a breakthrough.

In 2009, I was finding it difficult to focus on both my corporate job at Xerox and my family obligations. Incredibly, while watching Grace working with her teachers every day in my home, I came up with an idea for a "whole-child" educational game called, "I Can Do It! with Grace." It is based on behavioral teaching methodology and is now being used in school districts to help children with their academics, self-esteem, and social responsibilities. I also use it to generate awareness of and funding towards a cure for Sanfilippo Syndrome. It is my hope that this effective learning experience, which was inspired by Grace (with a lot of help from Julia!), will help create a better, healthier future for our nation's children. Through all of my conflict I have been given a very special gift. I am now my "own boss," which gives me the flexibility I need to be available for my children. I am also doing meaningful work that helps to find a cure or treatment for Grace, and I get to "give back" to society at the same time!

Luckily, I started my life with a very "full well" that came from a loving and supportive family, which has sustained me throughout this challenge. I am aware now, more than ever, that the physical, mental, and emotional health of the children in our country is extremely important and cannot be overlooked. I believe all individuals need to have every opportunity to fill their own precious "wells," and the younger we start, the better. We all know this is not always happening at home, so schools and communities need to get involved. Because of my experience, I have a very difficult time watching healthy children being "wasted."

Here is an excerpt from my website, www.gracecures.org:

On an airplane, they tell you to put your own oxygen mask on first before your child. This is such an odd concept, because any parent wants to place the care of their child ahead of their own! When given the devastating news of Grace's diagnosis, I learned quickly that I need to fight hard to take care of myself so I can be strong, and yes, even happy - for the rest of my life. This way I could be the best possible parent for my children! I remember watching the movie "Lorenzo's Oil" - the mother fell apart. I couldn't stand that! In real life, she actually passed away before Lorenzo did! I have learned that stress must be micro-managed and a spiritual view must be taken to rise to this type of extreme challenge. The mind, body, and spirit need to be nurtured and tended regularly. My personal practice, which includes exercise, yoga, bodywork, and mindfulness, has brought great blessings into my life, and with help and inspiration from my children, the "I Can Do It! with Grace" series of Whole-Child Educational/Wellness Games were born as a result. These games are now being used as home/school/community collaborative programs and are having a powerful, positive effect on thousands of children.

It is my hope that the lessons I have learned from Grace's special life will help to inspire healing in other children's lives. I may or may not be able to save my child... but I hope to make some "ripples" toward helping others to save theirs.

Needless to say, I have been "Graced." I have a precious and very special life and I am very thankful for it. We are all here temporarily, and sadly we are all going to lose each other at some point. None of us knows exactly what the future holds, and there are certainly no guarantees. I have been given the gift of intense realization of this fact, so I appreciate special moments more than most people do. Grace is doing well for now, and lives each day with joy and peace. I remember back in the worst days I said to myself, "If there is just ONE person handling this OK, I can survive." I want to be that person for others. Even if I achieve that and nothing else, I feel I have won this battle. But I am still hoping for a heck of a lot more than that!

About the Author

Joan Bellontine is a mom who founded Grace for a Cure, Inc., 501C3 not-for-profit organization to raise funds towards a cure for Sanfilippo Syndrome.

Joan also founded J. Grace Corporation, a company that provides "Life tools for Wellness and Grace-filled days." The "I Can Do It! With Grace" motivational games for children are sold via school districts or can be purchased online at Amazon.com. Please visit www.graceyourschool.com if you would like information for your school or would like to purchase a game for home use. The games are designed for children between the ages of three and ten and can be used to help children with their diet, exercise, reading, writing, and self-care habits. Check out our "Family Peace Promoting" game to encourage positive behaviors at home.

Currently Joan is working on getting her whole-child education programs into schools around the country. If you would like to help, an introduction to your school board president or decision making administrator would be a valuable and much appreciated gesture. Please call Joan at (516) 456-7575 if you can help in any way. Thank you!

To learn more about Sanfilippo Syndrome or to donate to Grace for a Cure, visit:

www.gracecures.org

Fellow Travelers

Sharing the Journey in a World That's Getting Smaller

by Dayna Fladhammer

"Today, the world is a much smaller place. I'm not looking for 250,000 people in a sea of six billion; I'm looking for them where I know they are."

Standing in the office of Vicki Modell a few years back, I realized the world is getting smaller every day. Vicki and her husband, Fred, founded the Jeffrey Modell Foundation in honor of their son, Jeffrey, who died at age 15 due to complications from Primary Immunodeficiency Disease (PI). The foundation is dedicated to early and precise diagnosis, meaningful treatments, and ultimately cures of the more than 150 types of Primary Immunodeficiency Diseases.

Having three children born with PI like Vicki's son, I've always admired her for her hard work and dedication. I realize, of course, that my own children will likely live much more complete lives because of her efforts.

Vicki and I stood talking about the recent first infusion of a mutual friend's daughter. We marveled at the medical advances that have given this little girl a life of hope. Hope that Jeffrey didn't have.

I'll never forget the sadness in Vicki's voice as she told me how she had longed for a friend who was going through the same experience she was when Jeffrey was diagnosed with Primary Immunodeficiency, and how she wished she and Jeffrey could have been members of the community that now exists. Vicki told me how happy it makes her to know that, as moms, we were coming together to help one another through this rare disease journey.

It was in that moment I realized this amazing woman, who has helped fund 100 centers for the diagnosis and treatment of Primary Immunodeficiencies, who has traveled the world helping to further this cause, a woman who has helped get billboards and radio and print ads telling the world about this disease, a woman who has helped shape the way children's lives will be saved, is at her core, a mother without her child. She is a mother who suffered intense loneliness because there was no community back then for this rare disease, a mother whose journey was isolating, lonely, and difficult. Jeffrey lived his entire life without meeting another child just like him.

How times have changed. Some of my children's best friends are also diagnosed with Primary Immunodeficiency. My daughter, Kate, has done multiple infusions with friends on Skype. Our son, Charlie, has talked to friends on the phone and has sent and received encouraging text messages during his infusions. He's walked another child through the first-time infusion process. Our youngest, Tommy, has helped other children across the globe cope with infusions by agreeing to be a part of a special book for children. We've spent weekends at conferences with other patients, we've met up with other patients at amusement parks, and I've sent my children to a Hole in the Wall Gang Association Camp, where they've roomed with other kids with PI.

It goes beyond physically spending time with other patients; it's the ability to find others who are also walking this journey of a rare disease with the advent of the internet. I have close to 100 other families I communicate with on Facebook, and that number triples when you add in Yahoo groups and a social networking site offered by the Immune Deficiency Foundation. This doesn't include the patients we've met in clinics, at Education Days, and other such events.

Today, I don't walk my journey alone. I don't wonder how to deal with a school system that is not set up for children with rare diseases. Instead, I ask the other parents. When I wonder what a new procedure will be like, I ask the teens who have already done it. Today, the world is a much smaller place. I'm not looking for 250,000 people in a sea of six billion; I'm looking for them where I know they are.

Last week, my three children spent 30 minutes on Skype with an adorable little girl who lives in Australia. A little girl whose mother I met through our blogs. A little girl who has the same rare disease as my children.

This young girl, still not even in kindergarten, was able to meet three other children who have the same rare disease as she does, who take the same medicine and travel a similar journey. On that day, as our children talked about what it was like to live with PI, the distance from Australia to Chicago shrank dramatically, and the world became a better place.

About the Author

Dayna Fladhammer is a Mom to her three children, Charlie, Kate, and Tommy, who were all born with a Primary Immunodeficiency Disease (PI). Her passion is helping others deal with and learn about PI. Dayna and her family travel to plasma centers to thank the donors of the plasma that is turned into life changing medicine for PI patients. She is the author of *This is My IVIG Book*, the co-creator of the Igi V Therapeutic Play Kit to help children cope with PI, and the editor of *Just Like Me*, a magazine devoted to children impacted by PI. Her family motto "To Whom Much is Given, Much is Expected" reminds her every day to give back to those who have given her children the gift of life.

To learn more or donate to the Jeffrey Modell Foundation, visit:

www.info4pi.org

Ellen's Prayer

Finding the Meaning of Hope

by Pat Furlong

"'Cure' is not a simple word, targeted at a single life."

When I was growing up, we had a lovely babysitter named Ellen, who started every meal with a prayer she learned as a child: "The Lord is my shepherd, I shall not want." Then she would add, "But I do," and recite a laundry list of wants and needs. She would look across the table with a silly grin and start to eat. At the time, my brothers and I would laugh, never imagining that one day we might find ourselves with a detailed list of needs. We were children, after all. The world looked simple from our shoes.

I looked forward to the day I would become a grownup. I made big plans. In many ways, I considered myself a princess, the youngest child and only daughter. In point of fact, I was spoiled. I expected success to be delivered at my doorstep. I could not imagine there would be a day when I would need Ellen's prayer. "Find yourself something to do and do it well," my family used to say. I felt capable, in control. I anticipated problems of course, the small hiccups of life. But in a certain way, I thought I had some sort of built-in insurance.

For a number of years, that vision worked. I was living the storybook life I had imagined. I became a nurse. I knew about patient care. I had confidence in medicine. My husband, a physician, was in private practice. We moved into our first home and had four children – two girls and two boys. Success seemed within reach. We had our eyes set on the future and carefully mapped out those plans.

On a sunny day in June 1984, adulthood arrived with a single word: Duchenne. In the course of seconds, the storybook version of my life was gone. The future was no longer clear. The power of this single word shifted the rotation of what we knew as Earth and changed every dimension of our lives.

Actually, the word hovered over our home for years, a cluster of letters unrecognized. Chris or Patrick would fall, as if their legs were swept out from under them. And there were reasons. Of course there were reasons. Excuses really. An untied shoe, the corner of the rug, a misplaced piece of furniture, and for that one single moment, the rationale seemed plausible. But I knew. I felt something in the pit of my stomach. Something was just not quite right and one by one, those letters took shape and formed a single word: Duchenne.

The first time I heard it out loud, it came from the lips of a physician. A photograph of that day is plastered on my heart. I was sitting on a chair in a very small exam room. The chair had no arms, nothing for me to hold onto. The room was shaking. The physician was looking at his toes. "Duchenne." He said it once, than again. "Duchenne." He called it a muscle disease. I searched the medical library in my brain, trying to remember what I once learned about muscle disease. Duchenne muscular dystrophy? Children in wheelchairs – a fuzzy memory while watching a telethon long ago. I could not retrieve any additional information.

His words were harsh, like the verdict in a murder trial. "Chris and Patrick have Duchenne." In the space of five minutes, this physician's words erased the life I was living. "Your sons will follow the predicted course of the disease. They will lose ambulation by the age of eight years. They will be unable to move their arms by 12 and will die in their teens." And he did not stop there. "Your marriage will fail and your daughters will resent the amount of time your sons require." The rest of the conversation became disjointed as the words and phrases began to sink into my brain. How could this be? Chris was six. Patrick was four. The doctor was wrong. I hated him. Surely there was something we could do, somewhere we could go. My anger surged. How could he or anyone say there is nothing to do, pronounce a death sentence on my sons, and send me home with nothing. I walked out of the office. The sun was shining. It surprised me. I thought the world had ended. From some unknown place in my memory, I heard Ellen praying: "The Lord is my shepherd, I shall not want. But I do."

I arrived home to visits from neighbors and kind words, bringing over gifts of food. It felt like a funeral, the death of my family. They had words which felt empty, words that fall out when you cannot make sense of what is happening. Words for a memorial service: "I'm sorry." "God gives problems to those He loves the most." "When life gives you lemons, make lemonade." "You are strong." I did not like the concept of a God willing to allow catastrophic illness in children, I have never liked the taste of lemons, and lemonade would not help my thirst. No one was dead. And strong? Well, that was just a word.

That night and most nights thereafter, I slept very little. I would wake frequently, sit bolt upright in bed, and visualize each letter of the word DUCHENNE being tattooed on my brain. Duchenne consumed me. I searched medical libraries, called physicians, and identified experts. I traveled across the country and the world. I went to the NIH and to Congress. I wanted to shout the word from the rooftops, hoping someone would hear, and know how to help. Over and over, I heard the words: "no hope and no help." I heard these words so many times I wanted to die. It made me wonder how anyone could say those words out loud and consider the conversation was complete, finished. We were talking about children, my children, and doing nothing was not an option. Why weren't they angry? Medicine had failed me. I wondered how it was that we are able to fly planes, set up space stations, walk on the moon, transplant hearts, and perform other medical miracles, but had no help for my boys?

In many ways, I felt like I was walking in reverse. I had failed motherhood. Mothers were supposed to dry every tear. I had no ability to dry tears, not my children's tears and not my own. Duchenne was the elephant in our home. It followed us everywhere. We worked hard to ignore it, tried our best to return to the life we knew to be normal, but life was no longer normal. My conversations centered around doctors, research, and the need to find some hope. Birthdays and holidays became bittersweet events, celebrations tempered with reminders that time was slipping away. My boys' lives were slipping away. Duchenne was winning.

I began to grow up and to learn the real meaning of Ellen's prayer. I set to work on a plan. I wanted to figure a way to buy five extra minutes of life for Chris and Patrick. I thought if I could just buy five minutes, I could repeat that activity over and over, layering those five minutes until I bought a lifetime. I found it very strange that while my own world was crashing down, I was changing. I was learning and growing. It seemed a contradiction. I learned about the world of genetics and rare disease, and arrived with a new vocabulary and a new family. My eyes were opened to delays in diagnosis, therapeutic nihilism, inadequate funding for research, gaps in knowledge, and the need to develop a roadmap capable of changing the world.

On days when tears would not stop, my children rescued me. I worried nonstop about our future and they would talk about an upcoming test or about weekend plans. My children grounded me, kept me on track, but Ellen's word continued to play like a song I could not get out of my head. I had my list of deals I attempted to broker with God and the promises spanned across the damage of that physician's predictions, first starting with my sons. "If you let them walk forever… I will…" And, "Ok, if they cannot walk, please let them move their arms…and I will..." "If you keep my marriage together, I will…" "If you help me with my daughters, I will..." Each deal had different parameters, different rules.

Strangely enough, Chris and Patrick were not praying the same prayers that I was or asking for deals. They were having fun, living their lives. Jenny and Michelle were living their lives. And my husband went to work and returned home each evening. I quickly learned that the 'deal' was up to me, and that 'cure' is not a simple word, targeted at a single life.

Ellen's prayer – "But I do," accompanied by a list of personal needs – changed, morphed, and molded into something greater than myself. I found hope in joining with others to create an advocacy group called Parent Project Muscular Dystrophy to promote research. For the past sixteen years, we have worked to create a world in which no parent will have to hear the words that I heard: "There is no hope or help for a child with Duchenne."

"There is an alchemy in sorrow. It can be transmuted into wisdom, which, if it does not bring joy, can yet bring happiness."

– Pearl S. Buck

About the Author

Pat Furlong is the Founding President and CEO of Parent Project Muscular Dystrophy (PPMD), the largest nonprofit organization in the United States solely focused on Duchenne muscular dystrophy (Duchenne). Its mission is to improve the treatment, quality of life, and long-term outlook for all individuals affected by Duchenne through research, advocacy, education, and compassion.

When doctors diagnosed her two sons with Duchenne in 1984, Pat immersed herself in Duchenne, working to understand the pathology of the disorder, the extent of research investment, and the mechanisms for optimal care. In 1994, Pat, together with other parents of young men with Duchenne, founded PPMD to change the course of Duchenne and, ultimately, to find a cure.

Today, Pat continues to lead the organization and is considered one of the foremost authorities on Duchenne in the world.

In 2010, Pat was named WebMD's Health Hero and was featured in *The New Yorker* as a "World Changer." She is the recipient of Research!America's 2008 Gordon and Llura Gund Leadership Award.

To learn more about PPMD or to donate, visit:

www.parentprojectmd.org

Thank you for reading *Uncommon Challenges; Shared Journeys.*

Please visit our website:
press.sireninteractive.com

There, you can:

- learn more about the thirteen authors and their causes
- order additional copies of this book
- submit your comments